Curves of Pursuit

Four dogs A, B, C and D are at the corners of a square field. Starting at the same time, and running at the same speed, A chases B, B chases C, C chases D and D chases A.

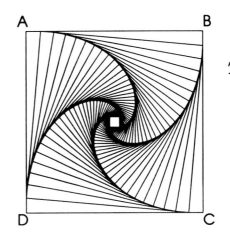

This is the result

Fit the squares together and we can make several different patterns, depending on whether we use 'left-handed' or 'right-handed' squares.

There are two basic ways of fitting squares together:

Shells

Sheaves of Corn

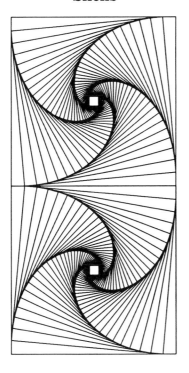

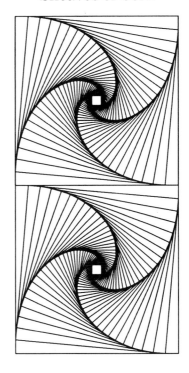

This is based on the first of these:

Of course we could start with different regular polygons:

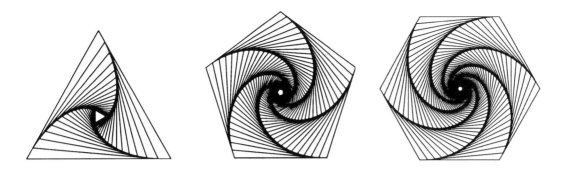

and they could fit together in all kinds of ways, sometimes the same polygon:

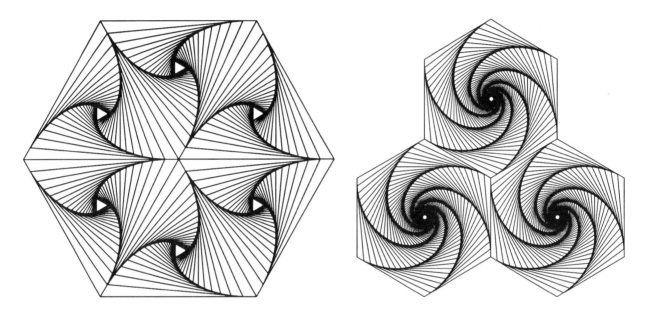

sometimes a mixture of polygons:

Polyhedra

So far all the patterns have been regular or semi-regular tessellations: the angles at each corner add up to 360°. When the angles add up to less than 360°, the only way to fit them together is to go into three dimensions. On the following pages are the nets for polyhedra covered with these curves of pursuit. Since the Greek for 'pursuit' is 'διωξισ' we can call these decorated polyhedra 'diokohedra'.

Constructing the Polyhedra

> You will need: scissors, a sharp point, glue.
>
> *The point of an old-fashioned pair of compasses is ideal.*
>
> *Use a glue that allows you to slide the surfaces.*

The net of a polyhedron is the flat shape which you cut out. You can photocopy the nets in this book on to coloured card and use a fixative spray before you make the models; or you can cut them straight out of the book.

To make your polyhedron simply cut out the net and fold it up.

But is it that simple? No.
The card will not fold cleanly and sharply without a bit of help.
So the first thing you must do is score the card.

Using a ruler, draw a sharp point along all the lines that are to be folded – including the lines at the edge where a polygon meets a tab. Hold the point at quite an angle and pull it towards yourself. Do not scratch the card, and be careful not to go completely through it. You should make a thin dent along the line so that the card bends neatly and exactly.

Score the net

Now you are ready to glue the model.

First make sure that each edge folds tidily.

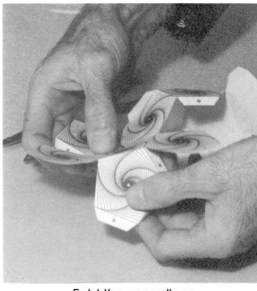

Fold the score lines

Then apply the glue, remembering two things in particular:

1: *If you use too much it will ooze all over the place and on to your fingers.*

Using, as your spatula, an offcut of card – there will be plenty lying around after the initial cutting out – choose two edges that are near each other and obviously need to be joined. Paste a tab sparingly and bring the surfaces together. When that is done there will be two more edges that need to be joined. Glue them.

Apply the glue sparingly

2: *Don't go too fast. It is hopeless to try to stick it all together at once.*

Wait for the glue to set before you move on, and make sure the whole time that everything is properly aligned. When you reach the end, it may be necessary to stick the last two edges at the same time, but until then be patient.

Be patient

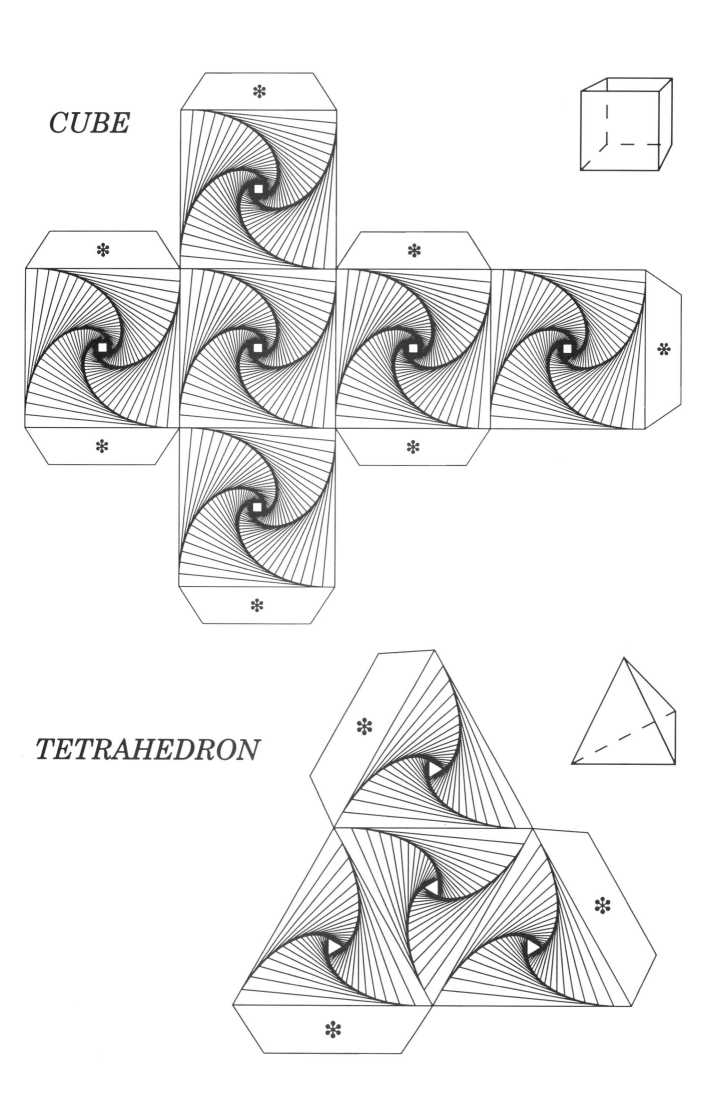

CUBE

TETRAHEDRON

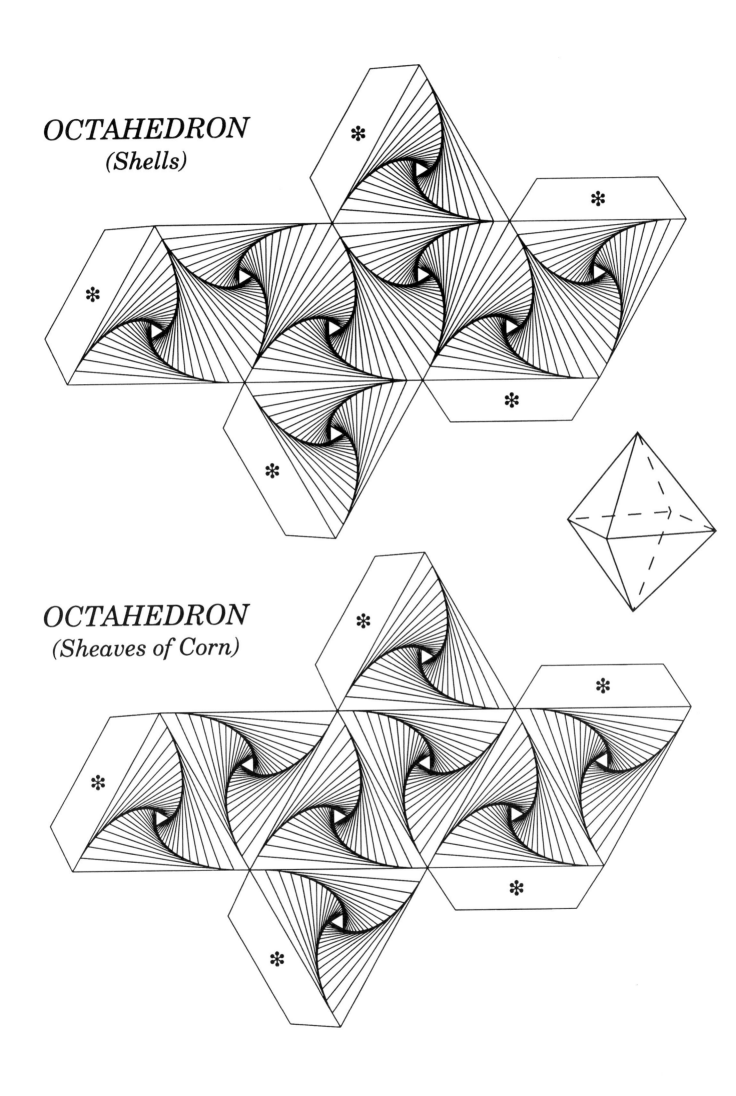

OCTAHEDRON
(Shells)

OCTAHEDRON
(Sheaves of Corn)

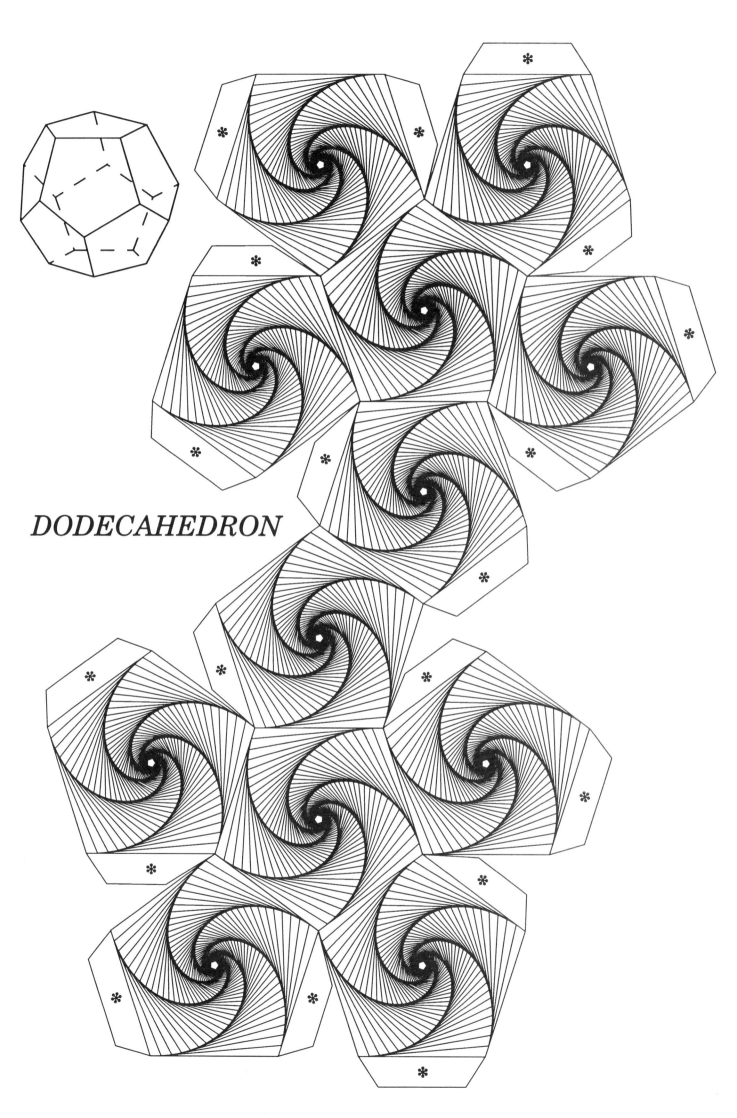

DODECAHEDRON

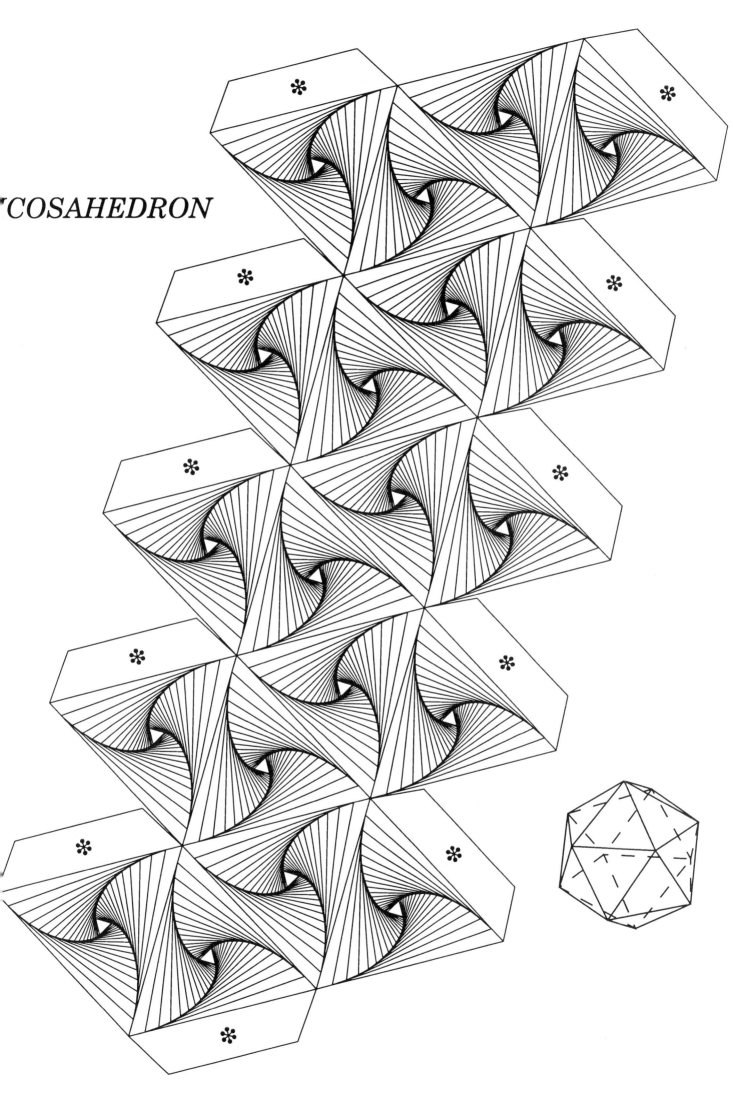

ICOSAHEDRON

CUBOCTAHEDRON
(Shells)

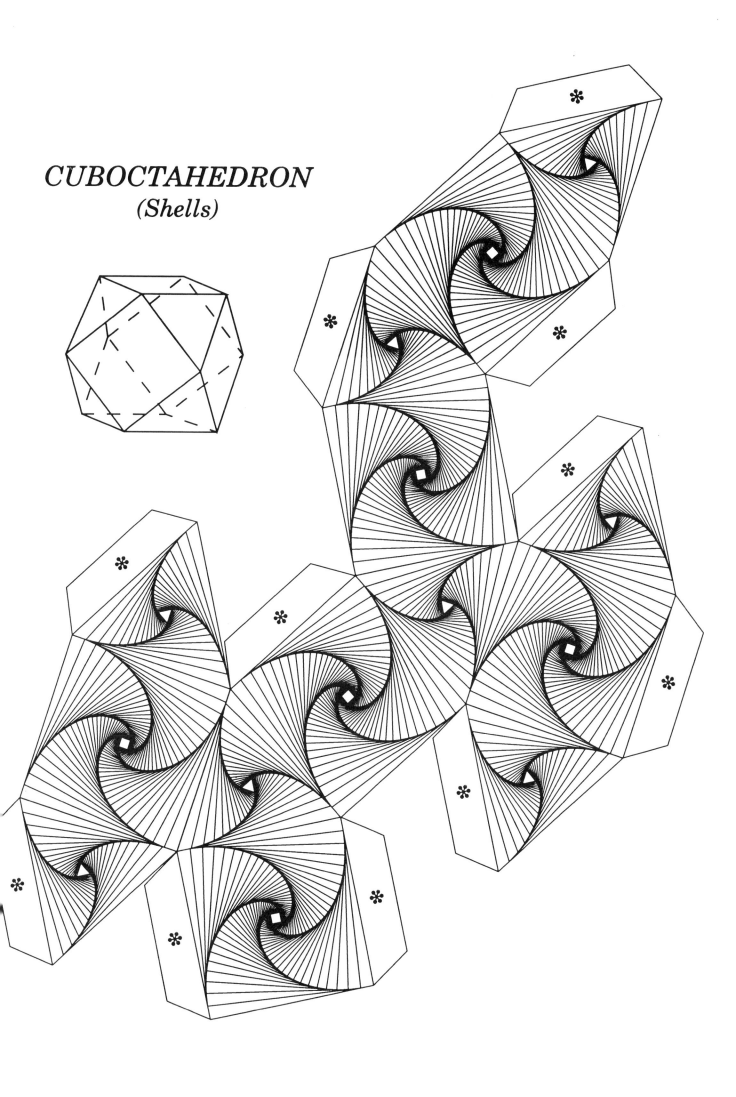

CUBOCTAHEDRON
(Sheaves of Corn)

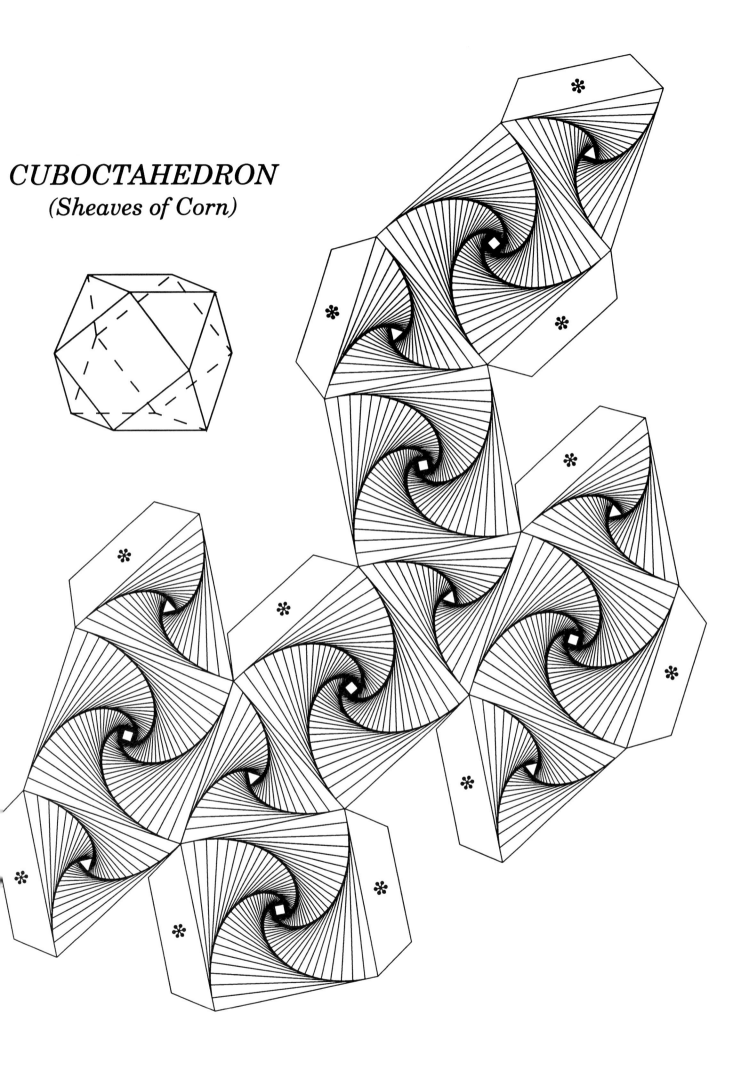

TRUNCATED TETRAHEDRON

TRUNCATED OCTAHEDRON

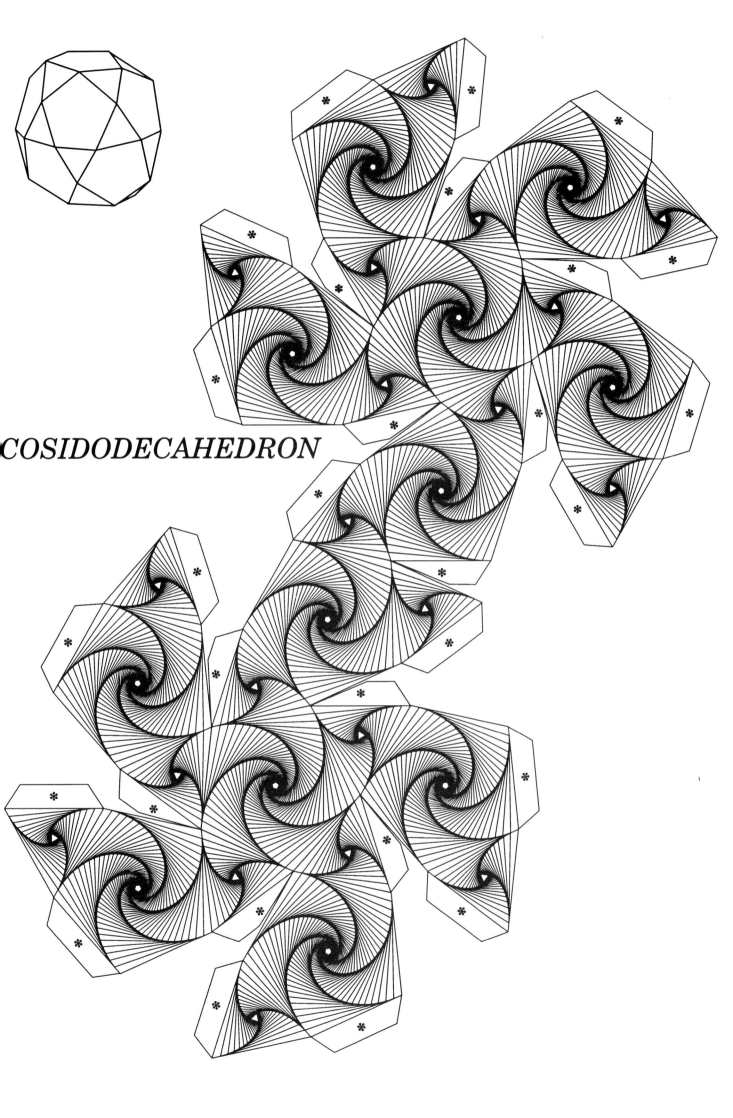

COSIDODECAHEDRON

RHOMBICUBOCTA-HEDRON

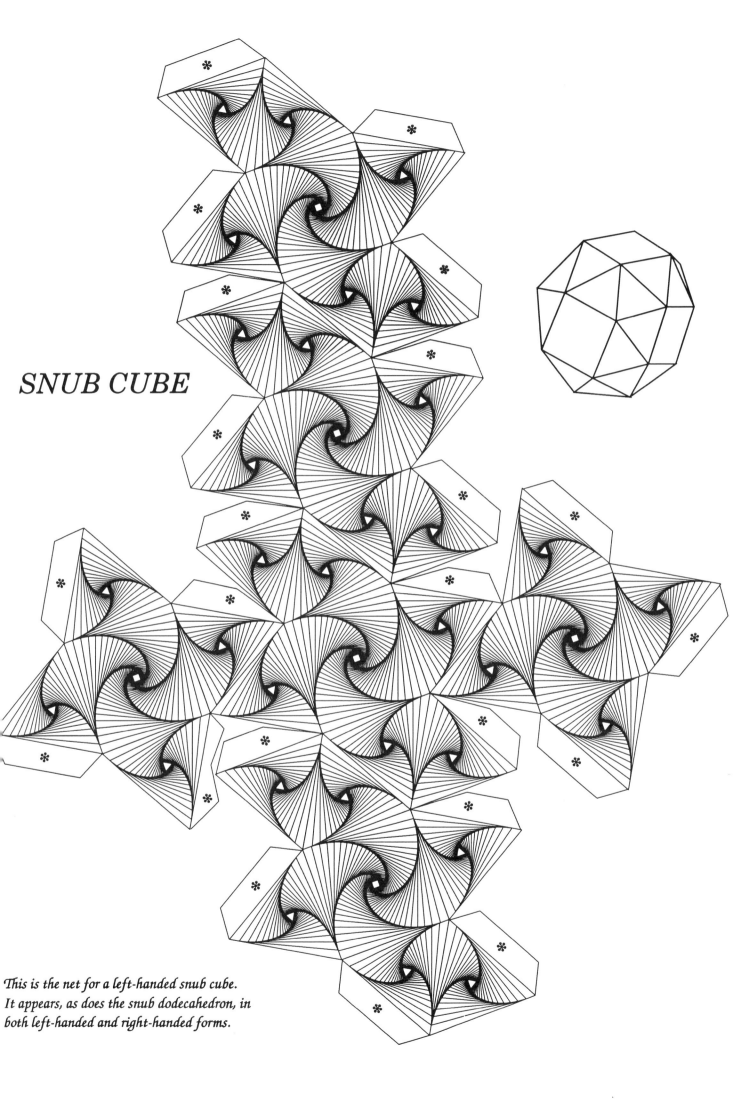

SNUB CUBE

This is the net for a left-handed snub cube.
It appears, as does the snub dodecahedron, in
both left-handed and right-handed forms.

STELLA OCTANGULA

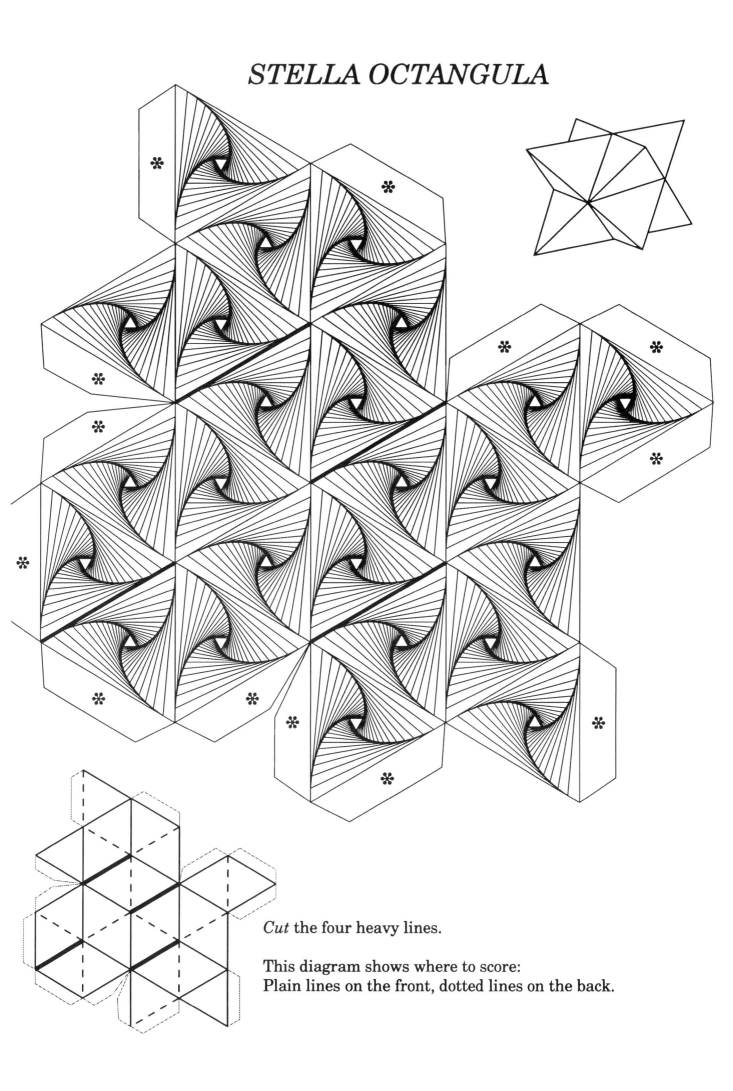

Cut the four heavy lines.

This diagram shows where to score:
Plain lines on the front, dotted lines on the back.

GREAT DODECAHEDRON

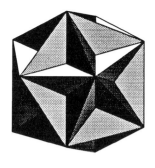

One way to see the great dodecahedron is as an icosahedron with twenty indented faces. Make these twenty faces separately and assemble them into the net of an icosahedron.

1. On the next page are twenty nets for the triangular faces of the icosahedron, more or less the same way up on the page as they are in the completed net for the icosahedron. Cut them out.

2. They are all indented. This diagram shows where to score: plain lines on the front, dotted lines on the back.
Score the twenty nets.

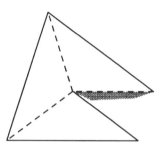

3. Glue the inner tabs and make twenty single indented triangles.

4. Assemble them to make the net of an icosahedron. You want to end up with this (the numbers are the same as the numbers on the twenty tabs which are internal to the icosahedron):

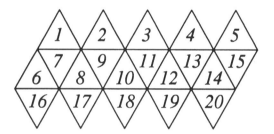

First assemble the chain 6–15, using the tabs with a black dot. Then attach 1–7, 2–9, 3–11, 4–13, 5–15, and 16–6, 17–8, 18–10, 19–12, 20–14, again using the tabs with a black dot.

Now your net for an icosahedron should be ready, with the tabs in the correct places. Make the icosahedron and you will have a great dodecahedron.

GREAT DODECAHEDRON

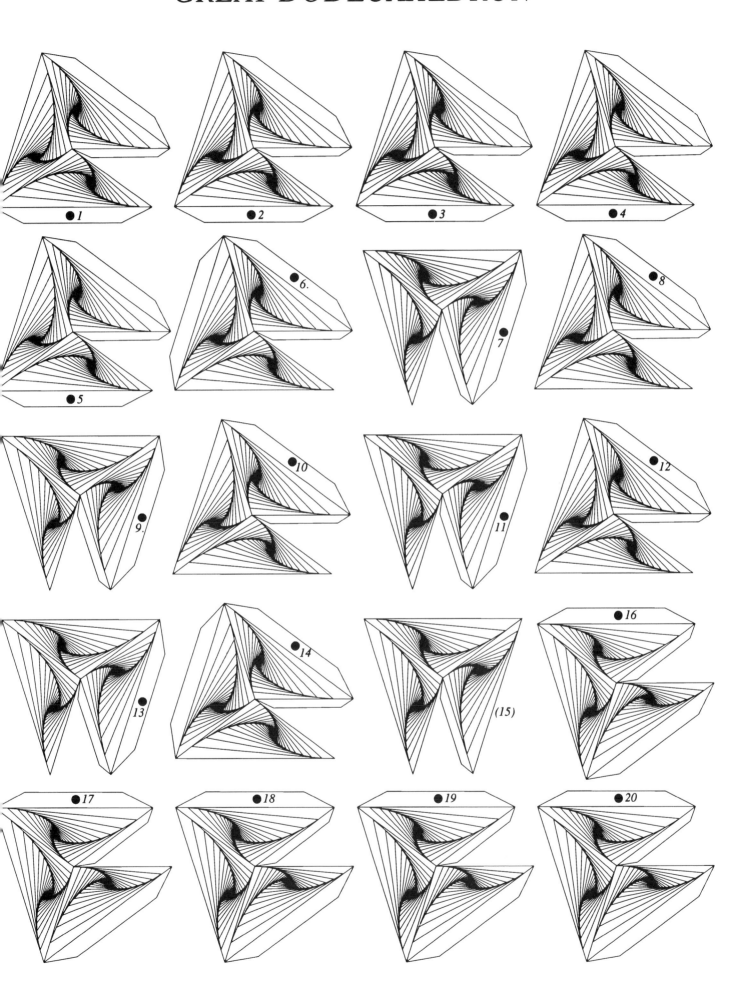

SNUB DODECAHEDRON (a)

Cut out the nets
on this page and
the next and join
as indicated
before you begin

JOIN THE TWO NETS HERE

Cut off this tab

On these pages are the net for a right-handed snub dodecahedron. It appears, as does the snub cube, in both left-handed and right-handed forms.

SNUB DODECAHEDRON (b)

Cut out the nets
on this page and
the last and join
as indicated
before you begin

JOIN THE TWO NETS HERE

Stick this tab
underneath
and make a
single net from
the two you
have cut out

On these pages are the net for a right-handed snub dodecahedron. It appears, as does the snub cube, in both left-handed and right-handed forms.

More Good Things from XYZPQR

Diokotessellation Posters
(set of 6, A3 size, laminated)

In the early pages of *Diokohedra* you will see tessellations of polygons which have Curves of Pursuit patterns on them. This set of posters uses some of these, and also some new ones.

Set of 6, £5.95

What is this?
(see over for the answer and for details of how to order)

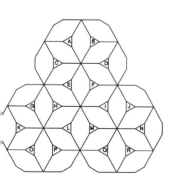

Diokotessellation 6.4.3.4

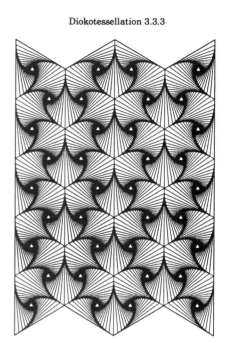
Diokotessellation 3.3.3

Diokotessellation 6.3.6.3

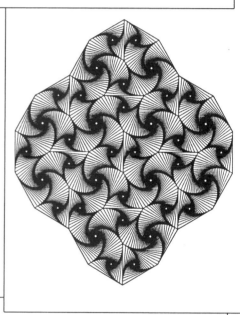

Diokotessellation 4.4.4.4

PRIME FACTORS G

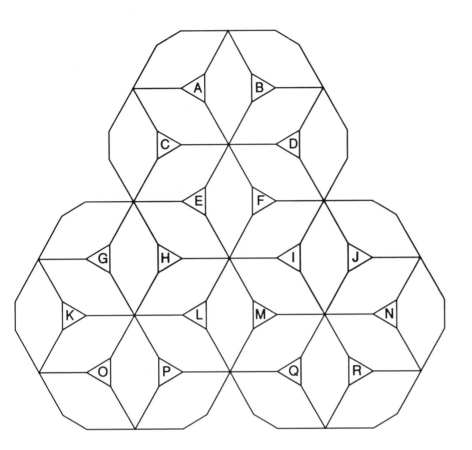

Each clue has three prime factors (some of which may be the same). Write these three factors in the three spaces around the letter so that each space contains only one number.

A:	66	J:	30
B:	102	K:	98
C:	195	L:	231
D:	273	M:	28
E:	110	N:	125
F:	70	O:	105
G:	12	P:	18
H:	242	Q:	42
I:	20	R:	45

One of '117 Crossnumbers and Number Puzzles'. This A4 size photocopiable book by W. Ransome contains 61 puzzles which give practice in basic numerical techniques, and 56 more tricky ones, presenting an assortment of number challenges on a wide variety of grids.